CHECK YOUR
VOCABULARY FOR HOTELS, TOURISM & CATERING MANAGEMENT

a workbook for users

by David Riley

PETER COLLIN PUBLISHING

First published in Great Britain 1995
by Peter Collin Publishing Ltd
1 Cambridge Road, Teddington, Middlesex, UK
© Peter Collin Publishing Ltd 1995

British Library Cataloguing in Publication Data

A Catalogue record for this book is available from the British Library

ISBN 0-948549-75-0

Text computer typeset by PCP Ltd
Printed by Latimer Trend, UK

Titles in the series

Check Your:

Vocabulary for Computing	ISBN 0-948549-58-0
Vocabulary for Medicine	ISBN 0-948549-59-9
Vocabulary for Business	ISBN 0-948549-72-6
Vocabulary for Hotels, Tourism	ISBN 0-948549-75-0

Useful Specialialist Dictionaries

Dictionary of Accounting	0-948549-27-0
Dictionary of Agriculture	0-948549-13-0
Dictionary of American Business	0-948549-11-4
Dictionary of Banking & Finance	0-948549-12-2
Dictionary of Business, 2nd ed	0-948549-51-3
Dictionary of Computing, 2nd ed	0-948549-44-0
Dictionary of Ecology & Environment	0-948549-32-7
Dictionary of Government & Politics	0-948549-05-X
Dictionary of Hotels, Tourism, Catering	0-948549-40-8
Dictionary of Information Technology	0-948549-03-3
Dictionary of Law, 2nd ed	0-948549-33-5
Dictionary of Marketing	0-948549-08-4
Dictionary of Medicine, 2nd ed	0-948549-36-X
Dictionary of Personnel Management	0-948549-06-8
Dictionary of Printing & Publishing	0-948549-09-2

To Order:

Contact your local bookshop or order direct from:
BEBC Distribution, PO Box 1496, Parkstone, Poole, Dorset, BH12 3LL
Tel: 01202-715555 Fax: 01202-715556

List of contents

Introduction

THE WORKSHEETS IN this book are based on the Peter Collin *Dictionary of Hotels, Tourism and Catering Management*. They contain a variety of exercises appropriate for students working in the tourist industry. Most can be used either for self study or in the classroom; there are also three pair work exercises.

The book is aimed at students with an intermediate level of English. However, some people who work in tourism have to read in English on a regular basis. This means that you may find lower level students with the passive vocabulary to handle many of the worksheets.

Specialist vocabulary
Students will sometimes tell you that they have no problem with specialist vocabulary: *'I know the English of my job'*. It is not a good idea to take this statement at face value. It can often mean that they understand the vocabulary of their job when they read it, in a manual or report for example. But *knowing* vocabulary involves more than simply recognizing it. Sometimes a student understands the meaning of a word when reading or listening, yet finds it difficult to remember when it is needed for speaking or writing. Students may remember the word, but use it incorrectly. This may be a grammatical problem, such as knowing that 'import' can be used both as a noun and as a verb. It may be a question of collocation: the way some words go together and some do not. We can go on a business *trip*, but not a business *voyage*. Then there is the question of the sound of the word. Can the student pronounce it? And does she or he recognize it when s/he hears it pronounced?

For these reasons - memory, use and sound - it is important to give students a chance to practise and play around with specialist vocabulary so that they can learn to use it more confidently and effectively.

In some ways, learning specialist vocabulary is simpler than learning general vocabulary. It is rarely necessary to decide if a word is formal or informal in style. And most specialist terms have one single clearly defined meaning.

But I know nothing about the tourist industry

You may be worried about trying to teach terms which you do not know yourself. There is a solution. All the vocabulary practised in this book is in the Peter Collin *Dictionary of Hotels, Tourism and Catering Management*, which gives definitions in simple English which students can read and understand. Many of the example sentences and definitions are taken from the dictionary. Make sure you have a copy of the dictionary handy for the students to consult. Never hesitate to refer students to a dictionary when they ask vocabulary questions: it is good learner training.

Photocopiable materials

All the worksheets can be legally photocopied to use in class, though if you intend to use most of the book with a class you will find it more convenient for them to buy a copy each.

Extensions

Many of the worksheets have *extensions* - pair work or discussions - based on the language in the main exercise. These worksheets can be set as homework and then followed up in the classroom.

Vocabulary Record Sheets

Encourage students to note the vocabulary they found useful at the end of each lesson, and to write example sentences showing how words are used and notes about meaning and pronunciation etc. Use photocopies of the 'Vocabulary Record Sheet', which you will find on page 42.

Communicative crosswords

At the end of the book there are three communicative crosswords. If you have not previously used this type of exercise, a possible procedure is given below.

1. SET UP. Divide the class into A & B groups, with up to four students in each group. Give out the photocopies of the crossword, being careful not to mix up the two versions. Give each group a copy of the dictionary. Go through the rules with them. Point out that some answers may be acronyms or may consist of more than one word.

2. PREPARATION. The students discuss the words in their groups, exchanging information about the words they know and checking words they do not know in the

A A	B B
A A	B B

Students work in groups, checking vocabulary.

dictionary. Circulate, checking that the work is going well and helping with any problems. This is an important stage: some of the vocabulary in the crosswords is quite difficult.

3. ACTIVITY. Put the students in pairs - one from group A and one from group B. The students help each other to complete the crosswords by giving each other clues

- *What's one down?*
- *It's a person who buys something*
- *A customer?*
- *No, it's a customer who buys a service.*
- *A client?*
- *Yes, that's right.*

A B	A B
A B	A B

Students work in pairs, co-operating to solve their crosswords

Alternatively, students can work in small groups, each group consisting of students arranged in two teams called A and B.

Make sure students are aware that the idea is to *help* each other complete the crossword, rather than to produce obscure and difficult clues.

We hope you and your students enjoy using this collection of exercises.

2

Recipe ~ crab soup

WITH THIS WORKSHEET you can practise some of the vocabulary of the kitchen and restaurant. It gives a recipe for crab soup.

o Before starting, check you understand the list of ingredients.
o Then read the instructions and find verbs which match the definitions in the box. For example, number 1, *to make food hot*, is 'warm'.

Crab Soup

Ingredients
½ litre of cooked crab
1 medium-sized onion
250 grams of any white fish
a little lemon peel
herbs
25 grams of breadcrumbs
50 grams of butter
the juice of ½ lemon
a pinch of nutmeg
175 ml of cream
1 egg yolk
salt & pepper

Instructions

1 Peel the onion.

2 Chop the onion finely.

3 Simmer the fish, onion, herbs and lemon peel in ¾ litre of water for about 20 minutes.

4 Strain the stock and put the breadcrumbs in it.

5 Mix the crab with the butter, lemon juice and nutmeg.

6 Stir the stock gradually into the mixture

7 Warm the mixture in a pan for 5 minutes and then liquidize it with a hand-held liquidizer

8 Combine the egg yolk and cream, stir in a little of the hot soup and return this mixture to the pan.

9 Stir until the soup is hot, but don't let it boil.

Definitions

1. to make food hot

2. to crush food to a soft paste

3. to reduce fruit, vegetables etc. to liquid

4. to boil gently

5. to cut into small pieces with an axe or sharp knife

6. to pour liquid through a sieve to separate solids from it

7. to remove the outer skin

8. to put things together

9. to mix up a liquid or food

10. to heat water until it reaches 100°C

Extension. Close the book and work with a partner. See if you can remember the whole recipe. Say the instructions, don't write them.

Based on the *Dictionary of Hotels, Tourism and Catering Management*
ISBN 0-948549-40-8

Opposites ~ travel & tourism

Exercise 1. Sort the words below into fifteen pairs. Each pair consists of two words with opposite meanings. For example: *close; open.*

add

advance · arrival

cancel · cheap · confirm · decrease

departure · disembark · double · early · embark

expensive · guest · host · incoming · increase · land

late · loss · outgoing · overcharge · postpone

profit · receive · send · single

subtract · take off

undercharge

Exercise 2. Check your answer to Exercise 1 and then complete these fifteen sentences using one word from each pair. Sometimes you may have to change the form of a word. For example: *take off; the plane **took off** two hours ago.*

1.   We've just _____ in Washington: can you send someone to the airport to meet us?

2.   If possible I'd like to _____ our meeting until Tuesday: Monday is going to be a difficult day for me.

3.   This bill's wrong: you've _____ me by £6.50.

4.   There was a technical problem with the doors on the aeroplane and the passengers had to wait twenty minutes to _____.

5.   I'm sorry I'm _____: I couldn't get a taxi.

6.   The hotel made a £1 million _____ this year, so we're paying a bonus to the staff.

7.   I'm calling to _____ my reservation for Monday; I'll be arriving at about noon.

8.   VAT is _____ at 17.5%.

9.   The hotel sends someone to the airport to meet _____ flights.

10.   If this holiday's too _____ you could consider somewhere closer to home.

11.   The hotel has accommodation for up to 2,000 _____ at any one time.

12.   I'd like a _____ room for myself and my wife.

13.   I'm booked on BA 152 to Budapest and I'd like to check the _____ time.

14.   The number of visitors to Spain _____ in the winter months.

15.   Could you possibly _____ this fax for me?

© Peter Collin Publishing
Based on the *Dictionary of Hotels, Tourism and Catering Management*
ISBN 0-948549-40-8

Recipes ~ gratin potatoes & apple crumble

WITH THIS WORKSHEET you can practise more of the vocabulary of the kitchen and restaurant. It gives recipes for gratin potatoes, a French recipe, and Apple Crumble, a traditional English dessert. The sentences in the instructions are in the wrong order.

i Check that you know the vocabulary in the lists of ingredients.
ii Read the instructions, and put them in a logical order. The first line in each one has been marked for you as an example.

Gratin Potatoes

1 kilo of potatoes; 200 gm Gruyère cheese; a little butter and garlic; a pinch of nutmeg; one egg; salt and pepper; ½ litre of milk

☐	Bake it in a medium oven for 45 minutes.
☐	Blend the egg and half the cheese into the milk.
☐	While it is cooling, peel the potatoes and slice them thinly.
☐	Put the rest of the cheese on top.
☐	Put the potatoes in the dish and season them with the salt, pepper and nutmeg.
☐	Rub a dish with garlic and butter.
☐	Stir the mixture into the potatoes.
1	Warm the milk to just less than boiling point and leave it to one side.

Apple Crumble

2-3 Bramley apples; 75 gm unsalted butter; 75 gm white flour; 30 grams brown sugar; a pinch of nutmeg; 2 dessertspoons of water; 100 ml cream

☐	Stir the sugar into the flour and butter mix; this is the crumble.
☐	Cook it under a medium grill until the butter melts and the top browns.
1	Peel, core and slice the apples.
☐	Put them in a pan with the water and nutmeg and cook them until they form a purée.
☐	Put the purée into a buttered dish and cover it with the crumble.
☐	When it has cooled, add a little sugar if necessary, and stir in the cream.
☐	Remove the puree from the heat and leave it to cool for five minutes.
☐	Meanwhile, rub the butter into the flour until it looks like breadcrumbs

Extension. Work with a partner. One person closes the book and writes, the other dictates one of the recipes.

© Peter Collin Publishing
Based on the *Dictionary of Hotels, Tourism and Catering Management*
ISBN 0-948549-40-8

Pronunciation ~ word stress

ONE OF THE keys to English pronunciation is *stress* - emphasis. For example:

■□□   **hol**-i-day   □□■   per-son-**nel**   □■□□ com-**mu**-ni-cate

□■□   de-**par**-ture   ■□□□ **pho**-to-co-py   □□■□ con-firm-**a**-tion

Find the three and four syllable words in these conversations and classify them by their pronunciation. There are 35 in total. The first one has been done for you as an example.

---

6 × ■□□

12 × □■□

5 × □□■

---

o Good evening, Can I help you?

• *Yes, I'd like to make a <u>reservation</u> for the excursion tomorrow.*

o I'm afraid it's fully booked. There are no more places available.

• *Oh, that's a pity.*

o If you'd like to leave your name with reception we'll contact you if there's a cancellation.

• *Oh. thank you.*

o Can you tell me something about the hotel?

• *Well, it's divided into separate apartments, each one self-catering.*

o What facilities do you have?

• *Well, there's a restaurant if you want to eat out, a bar and a supermarket.*

o Do you have a gymnasium?

• *Yes we do.*

o Is it convenient for the beach?

• *Oh, yes. Five minutes' walk.*

o What's the financial situation?

• *The main shareholder is an insurance company. They're happy to sell.*

o What about day-to-day operations?

• *The current manager has been running the hotel for eight years. She seems very effective.*

o How many employees are there?

• *Over a hundred including part-time workers.*

o And is it successful?

• *These are the occupancy rates over the last three years; they look very good.*

o What do you recommend?

• *Well, the avocado and prawn salad is today's special.*

o Oh, I'm allergic to seafood.

• *The asparagus with garlic vinaigrette is nice.*

o Garlic? I'm afraid garlic disagrees with me.

• *Why not have the tomato soup?*

o Do you think I'll like it?

• *I guarantee it.*

---

2 × ■□□□

5 × □■□□

5 × □□■□
reservation

Extension. Practise the dialogues with a partner.

© Peter Collin Publishing
Based on the *Dictionary of Hotels, Tourism and Catering Management*
ISBN 0-948549-40-8

Business ~ prepositions 1

EACH OF THESE sentences contains a **mistake**. The mistakes are all in the prepositions.
Find the mistakes and correct them. There are three types:

1. WRONG PREPOSITION	*on* We're meeting again ~~in~~ Tuesday morning.
2. MISSING PREPOSITION	*to* I spoke∧him about this last week.
3. UNNECESSARY PREPOSITION	I'll telephone ~~to~~ you tomorrow.

1. Our accredited agent in Bali is Mr Rodas: contact him and he can act in our behalf.

2. At the moment we are computerizing of our administrative systems.

3. The Plains Hotel is affiliated our group.

4. We need to meet again on Thursday: is 9.30 a convenient time to you?

5. The waitresses served to the 250 diners very efficiently.

6. We try to offer a flexible service, adapting the needs of our individual customers.

7. Thank you for your order, which will receive of our immediate attention.

8. The in-site courier is very reliable: we have been working with her for six years.

9. We only use reputable carriers, which means we can guarantee you an exceptional level in quality.

10. This item is not available in the shops: it can be bought only in mail order.

11. I'm afraid we do not have any double rooms available on the first week of August.

12. She runs a flourishing tour company organizing adventure holidays at senior citizens.

13. The new system becomes operational on June 1st.

14. I have faxed you my provisional acceptance the terms you offer.

15. He's the kind of person you can trust for to do the job, absolutely reliable.

16. We had to ask our lawyer professional advice about the contract.

17. Eventually we would like to install in an indoor swimming pool, but that's a long-term project.

18. He has the sole agency to Ascot car hire in this region.

19. After the fire they looked the policies and discovered that the hotel was uninsured.

20. Each hotel manager is accountable the regional manager.

© Peter Collin Publishing
Based on the *Dictionary of Hotels, Tourism and Catering Management*
ISBN 0-948549-40-8

50 foods ~ categories

THE LIST ON this page shows fifty of the commonest foods on menus. Do you know what each one is? Write the category it belongs to on the right. The categories are as follows:

MEAT   FISH   POULTRY   VEGETABLE   FRUIT   DAIRY PRODUCT   SEASONING

For example, the first food (*apple*) is a fruit. It has been completed for you as an example.

Food	Category		Food	Category
apple	*fruit*		onion	
apricot			oregano	
asparagus			parsley	
avocado			peach	
bacon			pear	
banana			pepper	
basil			pineapple	
beef			plaice	
carrot			pork	
cheese			potato	
chicken			raspberry	
cod			red mullet	
courgette			rosemary	
cream			salmon	
cucumber			sole	
duck			spinach	
garlic			strawberry	
goose			thyme	
grape			tomato	
grapefruit			trout	
haddock			tuna	
hake			turbot	
lamb			turkey	
lettuce			veal	
milk			yoghurt	

Extension. Work with a partner and design a menu for a restaurant offering either international cuisine or the cuisine of your country.

© Peter Collin Publishing
Based on the *Dictionary of Hotels, Tourism and Catering Management*
ISBN 0-948549-40-8

Cooking verbs

THIS WORKSHEET WILL help you to learn more of the vocabulary of the kitchen and the restaurant. Match the verbs on the left with the definitions on the right. The first one has been done for you as an example.

1	bake	*k*
2	blanch	
3	braise	
4	caramelize	
5	carve	
6	chill	
7	cream	
8	deep-fry	
9	dice	
10	flambé	
11	flavour	
12	fricasee	
13	fry	
14	garnish	
15	grate	
16	grill	
17	grind	
18	liquidize	
19	marinade	
20	parboil	
21	poach	
22	roast	
23	sauté	
24	slice	
25	steam	
26	stuff	

a   to cook food on or under a direct flame

b   to shred into very small pieces, using a rough metal tool

c   to decorate

d   to cook in oil or fat in a shallow pan

e   to pass food through a machine which reduces it to powder or pulp

f   to reduce fruit/vegetables, etc to liquid

g   to fry in a little fat at a lower temperature

h   to cook over a fire or in an oven with oil or fat

i   to cook eggs (without their shells) or fish in gently boiling water

j   to half-cook in boiling water

k   ~~to cook in an oven~~

l   to stew meat (usually chicken) with vegetables in a little water, which is then used to make a rich white sauce

m   to cut meat and poultry up at the table or in the kitchen for service to the table

n   to heat sugar until it becomes brown

o   to cook (meat or vegetables) in a covered pot with very little liquid

p   to cook for a short time in boiling water

q   to make cold

r   to mix ingredients together until they form a smooth mixture

s   to add spices and seasoning

t   to pour brandy or other alcohol over food and set it alight

u   to cut food into small cubes

v   to cook food in a deep pan of boiling oil or fat

w   to cut into large, thin pieces

x   to cook over a pan of boiling water by allowing the steam to pass through holes in a container with food in it

y   to put breadcrumbs, chopped meat, etc inside meat or vegetables and cook and serve them together

z   to leave in a mixture of, for example, wine and herbs for some time before cooking

Odd one out

IN EACH SET of words one is the *odd one out*: different from the others. Find the word that is different, and underline it. For example:

o *plane* . . . . *train* . . . . *coach* . . . . <u>*car*</u>

Car is the odd one out. It is a private means of transport; the others are all public.

1   chef . . . . cuisine . . . . commis . . . . plongeur

2   take off . . . . depart . . . . embark . . . . land

3   trip . . . . journey . . . . voyage . . . . holiday

4   telephone . . . . message . . . . fax . . . . mail

5   cheque . . . . invoice . . . . bill . . . . receipt

6   credit card . . . . . . cash . . . . currency . . . . traveller's cheques

7   egg . . . . chicken . . . . duck . . . . lamb

8   pastis . . . . scotch . . . . claret . . . . vodka

9   free . . . . complimentary . . . . gratis . . . . cheap

10 immigrant . . . . traveller . . . . visitor . . . . tourist

11 economy . . . . business . . . . law . . . . first

12 cable television . . . minibar . . . . swimming pool . . . hair drier

13 book . . . . magazine . . . . order . . . . reserve

14 rent . . . . purchase . . . . hire . . . . lease

15 single . . . . individual . . . . double . . . . suite

16 chambermaid . . . . . receptionist . . . . . . night porter . . . . . . guest

17 poach . . . . boil . . . . slice . . . . fry

18 goodwill . . . . creditors . . . . land . . . . buildings

19 patron . . . . customer . . . . manager . . . . client

20 lat . . . . lek . . . . yam . . . . baht

© Peter Collin Publishing
Based on the *Dictionary of Hotels, Tourism and Catering Management*
ISBN 0-948549-40-8

Business ~ prepositions 2

EACH OF THESE sentences contains a **mistake**. The mistakes are all in the prepositions.
Find the mistakes and correct them. There are three types:

1. WRONG PREPOSITION	Let's meet ~~in~~ *at* 10:00.	
2. MISSING PREPOSITION	The company's headquarters are∧*in* London.	
3. UNNECESSARY PREPOSITION	Have you received ~~of~~ my letter?	

1.   We are analysing of the market potential for golfing holidays.

2.   When we advertised for a new restaurant manager sixty people applied the job.

3.   The chairman has asked all managers to attend in the meeting.

4.   Communicating head office has been quicker since we installed the fax.

5.   He tried to contact his office with phone.

6.   The business is controlled for a company based in Luxembourg.

7.   We estimate current sales in only 60% of last year's.

8.   The government foresees a big increase in tourism in next year.

9.   This product is guaranteed during twelve months.

10. The accounts department handles with all the cash.

11. We are inquiring the background of the new hotel proprietor.

12. We interviewed of ten candidates, but did not find anyone suitable.

13. The company is spending thousands of pounds for launch a new travel service.

14. There is a system of bonus payments which are linked at your productivity figures.

15. The restaurant has maintained the same volume of business in spite the recession.

16. Not all the hotels in the chain are participating of this special Christmas offer.

17. We are promoting these new holidays on the TV, on the radio, on the press and on posters in the underground.

18. I certainly would not recommend to Miss Smith for the job.

19. Candidates should report our London office for interview.

20. The company transports millions of tons of goods on rail each year.

Staff

READ THE SENTENCES and match the underlined words and expressions with the definitions in the box on the right. For example *'casual'* in the first sentence means *'for a short period, not regular'*.

1. We have taken on some students for the summer period on a <u>casual</u> basis.

2. We organise most of our training <u>in-house</u> using experienced staff members.

3. These six rooms are for our <u>live-in</u> staff.

4. The accountant doesn't work for us: he's <u>self-employed</u>.

5. The staff <u>went on strike</u> in protest against bad working conditions.

6. I'm sorry service has been slow this evening - we're rather <u>short-handed</u> at the moment.

7. He was <u>assigned</u> the job of checking the sales figures.

8. He was <u>dismissed</u> for persistently being late.

9. Poor training and constant <u>hiring and firing</u> meant that the hotel achieved unacceptable levels of quality in service.

10. They <u>promoted</u> him from chef de rang to head waiter.

11. She has recently <u>qualified</u> as a hotel manager and is looking for her first job.

12. The head chef <u>supervised</u> the fitting of the new restaurant.

13. We <u>stopped</u> £25 from his pay because he was rude to the guests.

14. We had difficulty in <u>staffing</u> the hotel and had to start with fewer people than we needed.

DEFINITIONS

a) for a short period, not regular

b) to engage new staff and dismiss existing staff frequently

c) to follow a specialized course and pass examinations so that you can do a certain job

d) working for oneself

e) to give someone a more important job.

f) to give someone a job of work

g) living in the building where (one) works

h) working inside a company's building

i) with not enough staff

j) to provide workers for an organization

k) to remove an employee from a job

l) to stop working because there is no agreement with management

m) to take money out of someone's wages before they receive them

n) to watch work carefully to see if it is well done

Extension. Work with a partner and test each other. One covers the exercise while the other asks questions: *'What does casual mean?'*

© Peter Collin Publishing
Based on the *Dictionary of Hotels, Tourism and Catering Management*
ISBN 0-948549-40-8

Travel crossword

ALL THE WORDS in this crossword are connected with travel.

ACROSS

1   Journey on an aircraft (6)
4   'I'm going to Paris next week on a business _____.' (4)
7   Stage of the journey, part of the body (3)
8   Opposite to west (4)
9   Returning to the home country (7)
10 Place you keep cars etc (6)
12 Hunting expedition in Africa (6)
15 Temporary house made of cloth (4)
16 Journey on a ship going from place to place (6)
17 Group of ships, aircraft or road vehicles (5)
18 An engine and a set of coaches travelling on rails (5)
19 'You can get good prices ____-season'
21 One. two, three, four or five ____: rating system for hotels (4)
22 Money paid to hire a car (6)
23 Ride, rode, ____ (6)

DOWN

1   Cost of transporting goods (7)
2   'If you're going abroad you should take out medical ____.' (9)
3   Cars with drivers for short-term hire (6)
5   Type of ferry which cars and lorries can use (4)
6   What you intend to do (4)
11 Person travelling with a passenger (9)
13 Opposite of departure (7)
14 'You can't sit here: this seat's ____' (8)
17 'There's a fantastic view of the city from the top ____ of the hotel' (5)
20 'There isn't air-conditioning in the room, but there is a ceiling ____' (3)
21 Road, rail, air & ____

© Peter Collin Publishing
Based on the *Dictionary of Hotels, Tourism and Catering Management*
ISBN 0-948549-40-8

13

Hotel reservations

In these conversations customers are making a telephone reservation. Put the lines of the conversation into the correct order and number them in the boxes on the left. For example, *'Barnes Hotel. Good afternoon. Can I help you?'* is the first line in each conversation.

Conversation 1

☐ 3956 7254 9984 9876. And what's the expiry date?*

☐ Andrew Orpheo.

☐ 4 '99.

[1] Barnes Hotel. Good afternoon. Can I help you?

☐ By Visa.

☐ Can you give me the number?

☐ Certainly. O-R-P-H-E-O.

☐ Could you spell your surname?

☐ So that's a single room with bathroom for two nights, the 16th and 17th of June.

☐ Good. Could you give me your name?

☐ Orpheo. And how will you be paying?

☐ Thank you very much. We'll look forward to seeing you on the 16th.

☐ Thank you.

☐ That's correct.

☐ The 16th and 17th of June. A single room.

☐ What dates would you like to reserve for?

☐ With a bathroom?

☐ Yes, please.

☐ Yes, it's 3956 7254 9984 9876.

☐ Yes. I'd like to make a reservation.

Conversation 2

☐ £42.50 a night including breakfast.

[1] Barnes Hotel. Good afternoon. Can I help you?

☐ Could I have your name for the reservation?

☐ Davies.

☐ Double, please.

☐ OK. That's fine. We'll be there in half an hour.

☐ Single or double?

☐ Thank you. Goodbye.

☐ Thank you Mr Davies. We'll look forward to seeing you in about half an hour.

☐ What are your rates?

☐ Yes, do you have any rooms free for tonight?

☐ Yes, we do have a couple of rooms.

* Expiry date: last date on which a credit card can be used

Extension. Practise the conversation with a partner.

© Peter Collin Publishing
Based on the *Dictionary of Hotels, Tourism and Catering Management*
ISBN 0-948549-40-8

Opposites ~ tastes

THESE EXERCISES WILL help you to practise adjectives used to describe food and drink, especially words concerned with taste.

Exercise 1. Sort the words below into twelve pairs of words with opposite meanings. For example: *hot; cold*. (Note: some words have more than one opposite.)

bland

cooked · **dry** · **fresh**

fresh · **frozen** · **overdone** · **rare** · **raw**

salty · **sour** · **sparkling** · **spicy** · **stale** · **still**

sweet · **sweet** · **sweet** · **tasteless** · **tasty**

tender · **tough** · **underdone**

well-done

Exercise 2. Check your answer to Exercise 1 and then complete these fifteen sentences using one word from each pair. Sometimes you may have to change the form of a word. For example: *cold; can you heat up my meat - it's <u>gone</u> **cold**.*

1. With the fish we ordered a _____ white wine.

2. Take away this bread: it's _____

3. I don't like lemons, they're too _____ for me.

4. Could I have my steak very _____ I don't like it cooked for more than a couple of minutes.

5. We never use any _____ ingredients in this restaurant - everything is bought from the market on the day it is served.

6. Champagne is a _____ white wine produced in France.

7. This chicken is _____ : there's still blood in it.

8. Sushi is a Japanese dish of _____ fish.

9. _____ foods like peanuts and crisps make you thirsty.

10 This is very good - it's so _____

11 Can you take away this steak? It's so _____ I can hardly cut it.

12 I love _____ foods like chilli con carne and curries.

Air travel

THE EXERCISES ON this page practise some of the vocabulary of air travel.

Exercise 1. Put these sentences in a logical order. Use your dictionary if you need to. The first one has been done for you as an example.

☐ I bought a bottle of wine in the duty free shop.

1 I arrived at the airport.

☐ I checked in.

☐ We disembarked.

☐ We boarded the plane.

☐ I had lunch and watched an in-flight movie.

☐ Three hours later we landed.

☐ I joined the other passengers at the gate.

☐ I left the airport.

☐ It took off.

☐ I went through passport control.

☐ I went to baggage claim and picked up my case.

Exercise 2. Complete the sentences with the verbs in the box.

advanced	booked	delayed	departed	grounded	missed	routed
scheduled	stopped over	taxied	touched down	upgraded		

1. The flight departure has been **advanced** from 11:00am to 9:30am.
2. He _____ a ticket on the 19:00 flight to Zurich.
3. Because of bad weather, all flights via Vienna will be _____
4. The plane _____ from Paris at 11:15.
5. The meeting finished late and he _____ the flight.
6. Because of a mistake in the booking, he was _____ to first-class.
7. After the crash, all planes were _____ until their engines were inspected.
8. They are charging £1,389 for flights _____ London - Vienna - Bangkok - Taipei - Los Angeles - London.
9. We _____ in Hong Kong on our way to Australia.
10. The plane _____ across the runway to the finger.
11. After a twelve hour flight the plane _____ _____ in Sydney at 3:00am local time.
12. The flight is _____ to leave at 19:35.

© Peter Collin Publishing
Based on the *Dictionary of Hotels, Tourism and Catering Management*
ISBN 0-948549-40-8

Pronunciation ~ present simple

VERBS IN THE present tense add an s in the third person singular: I work, you work, he/she/it works. But the s has three different pronunciations. Look at these examples:

A: /s/, for example work<u>s</u>
B: /z/, for example sell<u>s</u>
C: /ɪz/, for example close<u>s</u>

Find the third person present tense verbs in these sentences and classify them by their pronunciation. Put them in the correct columns in the table on the right. There are 25 verbs in the 17 sentences. The first one has been done for you as an example.

1. The hostel <u>accommodates</u> groups of up to fifty hikers.
2. The overseas sales manager flies about 100,000 miles a year visiting the agents.
3. The courier arranges transportation to the airport, assists the tourists at the check-in point and escorts them to the gate.
4. After visiting the church, the party reboards the coach and drives to the hotel.
5. The size of the restaurant restricts us to twenty tables.
6. The company allows all members of staff to take six days' holiday at Christmas.
7. The bank attaches great importance to this deal.
8. The tour starts from the castle gate and passes through the park.
9. The store caters mainly for overseas customers.
10. He charges $60 an hour but gives an excellent service.
11. The whole population of the village lives off tourism.
12. Mr Duval owns 10% of the shares in the group and manages one of the largest hotels.
13. We want a room which overlooks the gardens, not the car park.
14. This ticket permits three people to go into the exhibition.
15. The plane takes off at 8am and reaches Hong Kong at midday.
16. Yanina supervises six girls in the reception area.
17. The town already boasts an 18-hole golf course and this new series of golfing holidays really fills a gap in the market.

Group A: 9 × /s/
accommodates

Group B: 9 × /z/

Group C: 7 × /ɪz/

Extension 1. Work with a partner: dictate five of the sentences to each other.

Extension 2. The same rule applies to plural nouns: /s/ cost<u>s</u>, /z/ sale<u>s</u>, /ɪz/ expense<u>s</u>. Work with a partner and find five example nouns for each sound.

© Peter Collin Publishing
Based on the *Dictionary of Hotels, Tourism and Catering Management*
ISBN 0-948549-40-8

Tax & accounts ~ adjectives

ONE WORD IS missing from each of these sentences. Which one? The missing words are all adjectives and they are in the box at the side of the page. The first one has been done for you as an example.

1. He bought a _duty-free_ watch at the airport.

2. When his accounts were audited they found more than $1,000,000 in _____ taxes.

3. After the first £3,500 and up to £28,000 your income is _____ at 25%.

4. As the business becomes more _____ your tax bill will increase.

5. The price is £1,250, _____ of VAT.

6. The project is completely _____ : it will need no subsidies.

7. Hotel keeping is still a _____ business.

8. As a non-profit-making organization we are _____ from tax.

9. We do not accept payments in currencies which are not _____ .

10. Your tax obligation will be, in _____ figures, about £350,000.

11. My accountant tells me that my membership fees at the golf club aren't _____ even though that's where I meet all my clients.

12. Keep all the receipts from _____ expenses - you'll need them at the end of the tax year.

13. In the UK children's clothes are sold _____ .

14. _____ profits were very good, but our marketing costs meant that we came out with very little money.

15. To calculate your liquidity ratio we need first to look at your _____ assets - cash, money people are going to pay you etc.

ADJECTIVES
allowable
convertible
current
deductible
~~duty-free~~
exempt
gross
inclusive
labour-intensive
profitable
round
self-financed
tax-free
taxable
unpaid

Extension. Work with a partner. Write a short conversation between a hotelier and his accountant. Use at least five of the words in the exercise above.

© Peter Collin Publishing
Based on the *Dictionary of Hotels, Tourism and Catering Management*
ISBN 0-948549-40-8

Cash or cheque?

MATCH THE EXPRESSIONS on the left with the definitions on the right. For example: i, 'hard cash', means 'money in notes and coins, as opposed to cheques or credit cards'.

1. Cash

i.	hard cash	=	card used to obtain money from a cash dispenser
ii.	petty cash	=	cash which comes into a company from sales or goes out in purchases or overhead expenditure
iii.	ready cash	=	machine which shows and adds the prices of items bought, with a drawer for keeping the cash received
iv.	cash desk	=	machine which gives out money when a special card is inserted and instructions given
v.	cash dispenser	=	money in notes and coins, as opposed to cheques or credit cards
vi.	cash register	=	money which is immediately available for payment
vii.	cash terms	=	paying a bill in cash
viii.	cash flow	=	place in a store where you pay for the goods bought
ix.	cash settlement	=	small amounts of money
x.	cash card	=	terms which apply if the customer pays cash

2. Cheque*

i.	crossed cheque	=	ask a bank not to pay a cheque you have written
ii.	uncrossed cheque	=	sign a cheque on the back to show that you accept it
iii.	blank cheque	=	pay a cheque into your account
iv.	bouncing cheque	=	exchange a cheque for cash
v.	sign a cheque	=	cheque which can be cashed anywhere
vi.	cheque card	=	sign on the front of a cheque to show that you authorize the bank to pay the money from your account
vii.	cash a cheque	=	cheque which cannot be cashed because the person writing it has not enough money in the account to pay it
viii.	endorse a cheque	=	plastic card from a bank which guarantees payment of a cheque
ix.	deposit a cheque	=	cheque with the amount of money and the payee left blank, but signed by the drawer
x.	stop a cheque	=	cheque with two lines across it showing that it can only be deposited at a bank and not exchanged for cash

* US spelling = check

© Peter Collin Publishing
Based on the *Dictionary of Hotels, Tourism and Catering Management*
ISBN 0-948549-40-8

Kitchen crossword

ALL THE ANSWERS in this crossword are connected to food and catering.

ACROSS →

1. To remove the bones from meat or fish (6)
4. _____ and butter (5)
6. Before the chicken (3)
7. A cold dish, eg lettuce, tomatoes... (5)
8. Oranges, pears, bananas, etc (5)
10. Dehydrated (5)
13. To put, for example, breadcrumbs and herbs inside meat and cook and serve them together (5)
15. Colourless alcoholic drink (3)
16. Pastry case with sweet or savoury filling (4)
18. Preserve using low temperatures (6)
20. Solid water (3)
21. A kitchen tool, eg: spatula, knife... (7)
23. Liquid poured over food to give it extra flavour. (5)
24. Warmed (6)

DOWN ↓

1. Give food to (4)
2. Type of beer (5)
3. Grilled bread (5)
4. Strong alcohol distilled from wine (6)
5. Example of 8 across (5)
8. The white part of meat (3)
9. Not suitable: 'This meat is _____ for human consumption' (5)
11. An item used in a recipe (10)
12. Evening meal (6)
13. Times when groups of people eat together in a restaurant: 'The first _____ is at one o'clock' (7)
14. 'Would you like tea or _____?' (6)
17. North American whisky (3)
19. Liquid inside vegetables or fruit (5)
22. Past tense of 1 down (3)

© Peter Collin Publishing
Based on the *Dictionary of Hotels, Tourism and Catering Management*
ISBN 0-948549-40-8

Anagrams 1

SOLVE THE ANAGRAMS by reading the clues and putting the letters in order to form words. Write your answers in the grid to find the mystery word spelled by their initial letters. The first one has been done for you as an example.

1. Number, street, town, country . . . . ADDERSS
2. Big enough for two . . . . BDELOU
3. System for sending letters from one place to another . . . . AILM
4. Between different countries . . . . AAEIILNNNORTT
5. Between evening and morning . . . . GHINT
6. Note asking for payment . . . . CEIINOV
7. High or low, summer or winter . . . . AENOSS
8. Spanish snacks . . . . AAPST
9. Where guests register in a hotel . . . . CEEINOPRT
10. Can be obtained or bought . . . . AAABEILLV
11. The end of the line . . . . EIMNRSTU
12. Translate speech . . . . EEINPRRTT
13. You can't make it without breaking eggs . . . . EELMOTTE
14. Loud sound . . . . EINOS

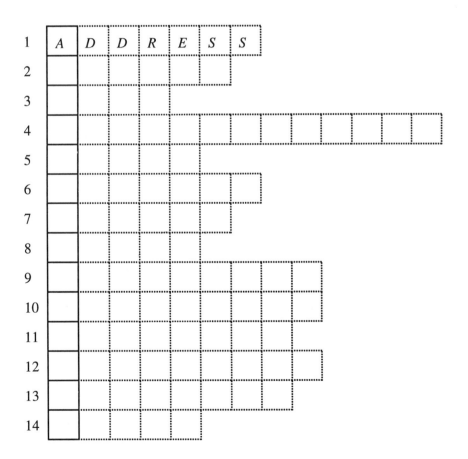

Mystery Word Clue: procedures

© Peter Collin Publishing
Based on the *Dictionary of Hotels, Tourism and Catering Management*
ISBN 0-948549-40-8

Finance ~ verbs

ON THE LEFT there are examples of twelve useful verbs connected to finance and accounts, on the right there are definitions of the verbs. Read the examples and match the verbs (which are in italics) with the definitions. Then write the infinitive forms into the spaces in the definitions on the right. For example, definition a, *to balance costs and receipts, but not make a profit* is 'break even', from sentence 3.

EXAMPLES	DEFINITIONS
1. Representatives have to *account for* all their expenses to the sales manager.	a. "_____" means to balance costs and receipts, but not make a profit
2. The books have been *audited* by Price-Waterhouse.	b. "_____" means to collapse financially
3. Last year the company only just *broke even*.	c. "_____" means to earn enough money to pay something
4. We are *budgeting* £100K for sales next year.	d. "_____" means to examine the books and accounts of a company
5. We do not make enough sales to *cover* the expense of running the shop.	e. "_____" means to explain and record a money transaction
6. The tour company *crashed* with debts of over £1 million.	f. "_____" means to help by giving money
7. Experts have *forecast* a steady rise in the number of tourists.	g. "_____" means to keep money, not to spend it
8. He *invested* all his money in a Chinese restaurant.	h. "_____" means to plan probable income and expenditure
9. All the airline's aircraft are *leased*.	i. "_____" means to produce as interest or a dividend, etc.
10. He is trying to *save* money by walking to work.	j. "_____" means to put money into shares or a business, hoping that it will produce interest and increase in value
11. The government has agreed to *subsidize* the hotel industry.	k. "_____" means to say what will probably happen in the future
12. Government stocks *yield* a small interest.	l. "_____" means to use a building, a piece of land or a piece of equipment for a period and pay a fee.

Extension 1. Work with a partner and test each other. One partner closes the book, the other asks questions. For example: 'Tell me a word which means to count something with other things.'

Extension 2. Think of another sentence for each verb.

© Peter Collin Publishing
Based on the *Dictionary of Hotels, Tourism and Catering Management*
ISBN 0-948549-40-8

Prices & payment ~ adjectives

ONE WORD IS missing from each of these sentences. Which one? The missing words are all adjectives and they are in the box at the side of the page. The first one has been done for you as an example.

1. We'll put a cot bed in your room for the baby - but you should know that there's a _supplementary_ charge for it.

2. We're planning a new range of Greek holidays at _____ prices to attract younger people.

3. If the car is damaged, the first £50 repair costs is _____ to the person whose name is on the rental form.

4. Most tour companies insist on _____ payment when a booking is made.

5. In the event of cancellation, I'm afraid the booking fee is _____ .

6. The entrance fee is _____ if you purchase $5 worth of goods when you're inside.

7. The prices in the catalogue are _____ of tax, so you'll have to add 17.5% to the total.

8. This price includes third party insurance: comprehensive cover is an _____ extra.

9. The price is _____ : you'll have nothing else to pay for the rest of the holiday.

10. The room rate is quite _____ considering the very high quality offered by the hotel.

11. We've got some last minute _____ offers - holidays so cheap you won't believe it.

12. We're looking for an _____ but good quality restaurant with a vegetarian menu where we can take the children and the dog.

13. If you take your holidays in November when there are fewer tourists the _____ rates are very competitive.

14. We'd like to visit Thailand but the cost of travel to the Far East is _____ .

15. If you wait and catch the train after 9:15 the _____ fare is much lower.

ADJECTIVES
advance
all-in
chargeable
cut-price
exclusive
inexpensive
moderate
non-refundable.
off-peak
off-season
optional
popular
prohibitive
refundable
~~supplementary~~

Extension. Work with a partner. Sort the words in the exercise into categories. Use any criteria you like. Then explain your choice.

© Peter Collin Publishing
Based on the *Dictionary of Hotels, Tourism and Catering Management*
ISBN 0-948549-40-8

Business ~ two-word expressions

COMBINE WORDS FROM A with words from B to make fifteen expressions connected with business and match the expressions to the clues below. For example, the answer to the first clue is *joint venture*.

A	B
balance	capital
bank · black	card · currency
business · cash · credit	flow · income · lunch
disposable · exchange · hard	margin · market · mix
joint · legal · marketing	rate · sheet · statement
profit · red	tape · tender
working	venture

CLUES

1. Very large business project involving two or more companies _____

2. Money coming in, money going out _____

3. Can be used to pay a debt _____

4. Price at which one currency is changed for another _____

5. Total cash and stocks etc used in day-to-day operations _____

6. Statement of the financial position of a company at a specific time _____

7. Currency which can be changed easily _____

8. Cost of sales ÷ sales income × 100 _____

9. What's left after tax and national insurance have been deducted? _____

10. True capitalism? _____

11. Product, price, place & promotion _____

12. Plastic money _____

13. Document showing current balance transactions in an account _____

14. Eating meeting _____

15. Bureaucracy _____

© Peter Collin Publishing
Based on the *Dictionary of Hotels, Tourism and Catering Management*
ISBN 0-948549-40-8

Anagrams 2

SOLVE THE ANAGRAMS by reading the clues and putting the letters in order to form words. Write your answers in the grid to find the mystery word spelled by their initial letters. The first one has been done for you as an example.

1. Book where you write appointments . . . . ADIRY
2. To bring goods from abroad . . . . IMOPRT
3. To bring goods from abroad illegally . . . . EGGLMSU
4. More than usual . . . . AERTX
5. 1,000,000 . . . . IILLMNO
6. First meal of the day . . . . AABEFKRST
7. Green fruit with no sugar . . . . AACDOOV
8. Place to eat . . . . AAENRRSTTU
9. Place to cook . . . . CEHIKNT
10. Place to live . . . . AACCDIMMNOOOT
11. Measurement of heat . . . . AEEEMPRRTTU
12. Payment made for using money . . . . EEINRSTT
13. Choice, alternative, possibility . . . . INOOPT
14. Scandinavian . . . . CDINOR

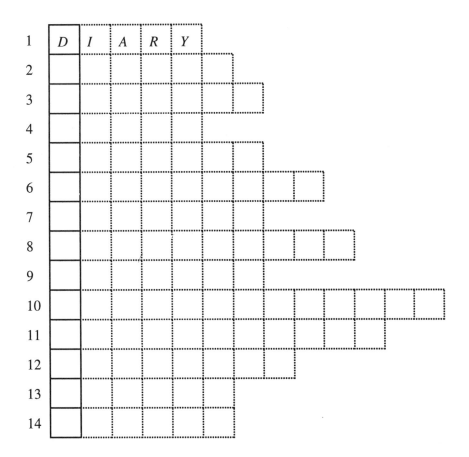

Mystery Word Clue: 'Goodbye. We hope you enjoyed your flight.'

© Peter Collin Publishing
Based on the *Dictionary of Hotels, Tourism and Catering Management*
ISBN 0-948549-40-8

Word association

ONE WORD IS associated with each set of four words below. For example, 'holiday' could connect *pay, camp, resort* and *season* (holiday camp, holiday pay, holiday resort, holiday season. What are the missing words below?

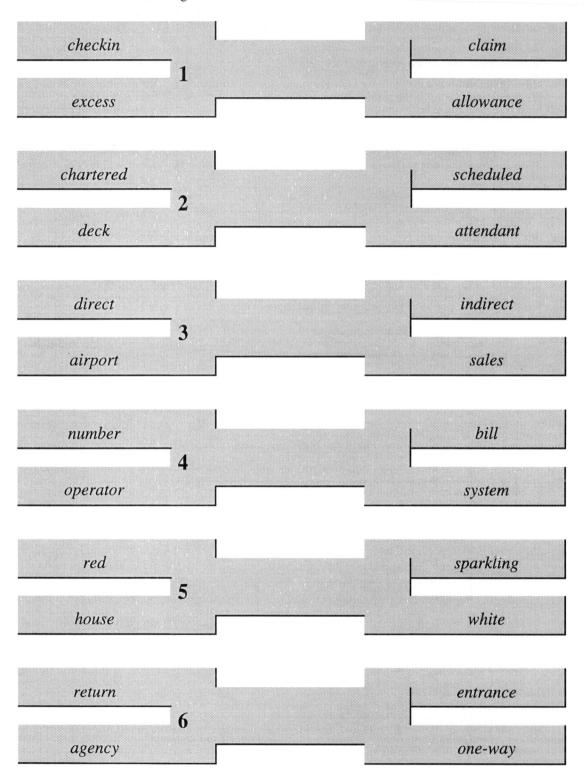

checkin	**1**	claim
excess		allowance

chartered	**2**	scheduled
deck		attendant

direct	**3**	indirect
airport		sales

number	**4**	bill
operator		system

red	**5**	sparkling
house		white

return	**6**	entrance
agency		one-way

Extension. Think of two more words for each group.

Based on the *Dictionary of Hotels, Tourism and Catering Management*
ISBN 0-948549-40-8

Active to passive

CHANGE THE SENTENCES from active to passive. For example:

ACTIVE:	*They admit children at half price.*
PASSIVE:	*Children are admitted at half price.*

1. We allocate 10% of revenue to publicity.

    . . . .

2. They forbid women to go into the temple.

    . . . .

3. Someone broke into my hotel room and stole my wallet.

    . . . .

4. A guide showed the visitors around the cathedral.

    . . . .

5. We have broken expenditure down into hotel, travel and entertainment costs.

    . . . .

6. They will hold the wedding reception in the Blue Room.

    . . . .

7. We are allocating £2,500 to furnishing the guests' lounge

    . . . .

8. When they made the first booking they were still building the hotel.

    . . . .

9. They are renovating the dining rooms for the new season.

    . . . .

10. They will launch a new travel service next month.

    . . . .

11. They transferred me to another flight because they had overbooked the one I was on.

    . . . .

12. You need to service the coach every six months.

    . . . .

13. They would have cancelled the trip if they had received this information earlier.

    . . . .

14. They will have furnished the hotel by the end of August.

    . . . .

© Peter Collin Publishing
Based on the *Dictionary of Hotels, Tourism and Catering Management*
ISBN 0-948549-40-8

Abbreviations

TEST YOUR ABBREVIATIONS. All these abbreviations are connected with tourism. What do they stand for? Check the ones you don't know in the dictionary.

1. g&t . . . .

2. e&oe . . . .

3. ETA . . . .

4. PR . . . .

5. EFT . . . .

6. F&B . . . .

7. ECU . . . .

8. asap . . . .

9. AGM . . . .

10. VAT . . . .

11. SWOT . . . .

12. STOL . . . .

13. POS . . . .

14 IT . . . .

15. L/C . . . .

16. APR . . . .

17. b&b . . . .

18. CRS . . . .

19. ono . . . .

20. BBQ . . . .

Extension. Work with a partner and test each other. One partner closes the book, the other asks questions. For example: *'What does g and t stand for?'*

© Peter Collin Publishing
Based on the *Dictionary of Hotels, Tourism and Catering Management*
ISBN 0-948549-40-8

Marketing ~ adjectives

ONE WORD IS missing from each of these sentences. Which one? The missing words are all adjectives and they are in the box at the side of the page. The first one has been done for you as an example.

1. The South Coast is one of the most ____*popular*____ areas for holidays - we sold hundreds of holidays there last year.

2. The TV advert gave a _____ telephone number which customers could call to place orders.

3. We offer better prices off-season to try to compensate for _____ fluctuations in demand.

4. Majorca used to be fairly expensive, but competition between hoteliers has driven it _____ .

5. October is a _____ month for us: our busiest time is in the summer.

6. The sales director sends _____ letters to all the contacts after each visit.

7. The _____ groups this type of holiday will appeal to will mainly be better-off middle class people: As and B1s.

8. The _____ fare (available until March) offers a £100 saving for passengers who book the airline's early morning flight and return the same day.

9. The _____ market - business travellers plus tourists from other parts of the UK - is a twelve month a year business and we couldn't survive without it.

10. Our _____ occupancy rates for the hotels in southern Europe over the last three months was 85%.

11. We've been open for ten years now and we have an established base of _____ customers.

12. Each guest receives a _____ box of chocolates when they check in to the hotel for two days or more.

13. In a recession people have less _____ income and the tourist industry suffers from a drop in demand.

14. We have to be extremely careful in setting prices for these tours, as the demand for this type of holiday is very _____ .

15. We'd like to move the resort _____ and attract fewer, but higher-spending, tourists.

ADJECTIVES
average
backup
complimentary
discretionary
domestic
down-market
elastic
~~popular~~
promotional
regular
seasonal
slack
socio-economic
toll-free
upmarket

Extension. Work with a partner. Talk about the marketing policy of your national tourist board(s).

© Peter Collin Publishing
Based on the *Dictionary of Hotels, Tourism and Catering Management*
ISBN 0-948549-40-8

Prices & payments ~ verbs

ON THE LEFT there are examples of twelve useful verbs connected to payment and prices, and on the right there are definitions of the verbs. Read the examples and match the verbs (which are in italics) with the definitions. Then write the infinitive forms into the spaces in the definitions on the right. For example, definition a, *to compare prices before buying*, is 'shop around' from sentence 11.

EXAMPLES	DEFINITIONS
1. Do you *accept* payment by cheque?	a) "_____" means to compare prices before buying.
2. They spent two hours *bargaining* about the price.	b) "_____" means to count something with other things.
3. The hotel *deducted* $3 from the room price.	c) "_____" means to decide how much has to be paid for a product or service
4. Tour operators are *discounting* prices on package holidays.	d) "_____" means to discuss the price for something
5. The room is £40 *including* breakfast.	e) "_____" means to estimate or calculate the probable cost of something
6. We *invoiced* you for this amount on November 10th.	f) "_____" means to make a deposit
7. He *paid* £50 *down* and the rest in monthly instalments	g) "_____" means to pay back money
8. We have *priced* these holidays competitively at under £250.	h) "_____" means to reduce prices to increase sales
9. Can you *quote* for supplying 200 cases of wine?	i) "_____" means to reduce sharply
10. All money will be *refunded* if the tour is cancelled.	j) "_____" means to remove money from a total
11. It pays to *shop around* when you are planning to fly to the States.	k) "_____" means to send a note asking for payment
12. The company has *slashed* prices on tours to Turkey.	l) "_____" means to take something which is being offered

Extension 1. Work with a partner and test each other. One partner closes the book, the other asks questions. For example: 'Tell me a word which means *to count something with other things.*'

Extension 2. Think of another sentence for each verb.

© Peter Collin Publishing
Based on the *Dictionary of Hotels, Tourism and Catering Management*
ISBN 0-948549-40-8

Food & drink ~ French in English

ENGLISH USES A lot of words from other languages, especially French, and especially French in the language of the restaurant. Complete these sentences using the words and phrases in the box on the right. For example, the missing word from sentence 1 is *brut*.

1. I like champagne, but this one is rather sweet for me. I prefer _____ .

2. I'm glad you enjoyed the meal. Would you like a _____ ?

3. Here's the menu. We also have a _____ which is mackerel in white wine with spring onions.

4. My first job in the kitchen was as a _____ . Nowadays we have a dishwashing machine.

5. We serve the salad with a simple _____ .

6. I usually have the set menu, but this is a special occasion. Let's go _____ .

7. I love apple pie _____ - it's the combination of hot and cold that I find irresistible.

8. This is an excellent red, bottled on the _____ .

9. The restaurant has improved enormously since Larry Duval became the _____ .

10. We're investing a lot of money to create a restaurant which offers a genuinely _____ service.

11. Add some ground chilli, but not too much. Just a _____ .

12. Red wine should normally be served _____ .

13. If you want to have dinner in the hotel we have a special _____ price which is very economical.

14. We _____ the mushrooms in butter with garlic and black pepper.

15. A real _____ chef can make very good money in London.

16. There's the _____ which is a set price of £18.90 for three courses.

17. They complained to the _____ about the service they had received.

18. We use a _____ to flavour the soup.

19. I'm not crazy about _____ - I'm usually still hungry after I finish dinner.

20. While we were looking at the menu we were served Atlantic prawns with mayonnaise and an endive salad as an _____ .

21. Almost everything is prepared in our own kitchen except that we use a _____ for patisserie.

French Words & Phrases

à la mode

à la carte

bouquet garni

brut

chambré

château

chef de cuisine

cordon bleu

de luxe

digestif

en pension

hors-d'oeuvre

maître d'hôtel

nouvelle cuisine

plat du jour

plongeur

sauté

soupçon

table d'hôte

traiteur

vinaigrette

© Peter Collin Publishing
Based on the *Dictionary of Hotels, Tourism and Catering Management*
ISBN 0-948549-40-8

Pronunciation ~ past simple

REGULAR VERBS HAVE three different pronunciations in the past tense (or the past participle). The difference is in the sound you use for the ending. For example:

A: /t/, for example work<u>ed</u>
B: /d/, for example clos<u>ed</u>
C: /ɪd/, for example start<u>ed</u>

Find the past tense verbs in these sentences and classify them by their pronunciation. Put them in the correct columns in the table on the right. There are 29 verbs in the 20 sentences. The first has been done as an example.

1. She <u>addressed</u> the letter to the hotel manager.
2. Because of fog, flights have been diverted to Manchester.
3. The guide warned us that there might be snakes in the ruins.
4. The trade delegates visited the Ministry of Commerce
5. We cancelled the project when our German partners backed out.
6. They have updated their guide to Greece and included three new destinations.
7. I faxed the documents and telephoned to check they had received them.
8. The pilot announced that there would be turbulence and asked us to fasten our safety belts.
9. We changed our flight as the travel agency had double-booked us.
10. All rooms are equipped with hair-dryers.
11. They smuggled the computer disks into the country.
12. We translated the brochure into Japanese.
13. He trained as a scuba-diving instructor.
14. The party were allocated rooms in the hotel annex.
15. We have recruited six girls to act as hostesses at the Computer Show.
16. The sales figures had not been processed so he postponed the meeting to the next day.
17. They called to say that the date for the reception has been fixed for 10th October.
18. The government lifted the ban on imports from Japan
19. He recommended a good bar in the High Street.
20. They invited all the agents to a party where they launched their new winter sports catalogue.

Extension. Work with a partner: dictate five of the sentences to each other.

Group A: 10 × /t/
addressed

Group B: 9 × /d/

Group C: 10 × /ɪd/

© Peter Collin Publishing
Based on the *Dictionary of Hotels, Tourism and Catering Management*
ISBN 0-948549-40-8

Hotels ~ adjectives

ONE WORD IS missing from each of these sentences. Which one? The missing words are all adjectives and they are in the box at the side of the page. The first one has been done for you as an example.

1. The guest rooms have been refurnished with ___luxurious___ carpets and fittings.

2. I'm sorry that you haven't been happy with your hotel: we'll find you _____ accommodation immediately.

3. In addition to the main restaurant there is a _____ cafeteria and a bar.

4. The best conference hotels provide a _____ member of staff for each conference to liaise with the organizer and ensure the event proceeds smoothly.

5. If you can't put us in _____ rooms, could we at least have rooms on the same floor?

6. Some of the rooms look out onto a main road, so I'm afraid they might be a little _____ .

7. We are a city centre hotel mainly catering to _____ guests.

8. It's a south-facing room so it's nice and _____ all day.

9. From the terrace, you have a marvellous view over the _____ countryside.

10. I'm sorry: we haven't got any _____ rooms. Have you tried the Grand?

11. The hotel has 25 bedrooms, all with _____ bathrooms.

12. Our restaurant is open both to _____ and to guests.

13. The hotel is divided into separate _____ apartments.

14. There are more _____ chairs in the lounge, if you find the dining room chairs too hard.

15. The hotel has _____ gardens for the exclusive use of guests.

ADJECTIVES

adjoining

alternative

comfortable

dedicated

en suite

~~luxurious~~

noisy

non-residents

private

self-catering

self-service

short-stay

sunny

surrounding

vacant

Extension. Work with a partner. Discuss what the qualities of a good hotel are.

© Peter Collin Publishing
Based on the *Dictionary of Hotels, Tourism and Catering Management*
ISBN 0-948549-40-8

Slang

SLANG (for example: 'ad' for 'advertisement') can make your conversation sound more natural if you use it at the right time. We do **not** use slang very often with customers, but between colleagues it is very normal. Find the slang words and expressions in the seven conversations below and match them to the definitions on the right.

i   o   Well, you know how they got that contract.
    •   *I've heard they gave the minister a backhander.*
    o   Yes. And it's the tax payer who picks up the tab in the end.
    •   *Absolutely.*

ii   o   Problem with room 213.
    •   *Not another skipper?*
    o   Afraid so.
    •   *That's the third this week.*

iii   o   How much did you pay for your ticket?
    •   *A hundred and twenty. What about you?*
    o   Seventy-five. I went to a bucket shop.
    •   *Well, I'd rather go to someone reputable than one of these fly-by-night operations.*

iv   o   If you don't speed up they'll fire you.
    •   *I can't. I'm too tired.*
    o   Why? What have you been up to?
    •   *I've been moonlighting in that new French restaurant all week.*

v   o   I'm starving.
    •   *Do you feel like going out?*
    o   No, not really. Why don't we phone for a takeaway?
    •   *Good idea.*

vi   o   Look at the menu.
    •   *What about it?*
    o   Well, it's a bit steep, isn't it?
    •   *What do you expect? This is a good restaurant.*

vii   o   Here's your ticket.
    •   *Cheers.*
    o   Where's Jenny?
    •   *She's in the loo.*

Find the words which mean:

1   Excessive.

2   A bribe, money given to someone to get him to help you.

3   Thank you. (Also: Good health!).

4   To do a second job for cash (often in the evening).

5   Very hungry.

6   Toilet.

7   Unbonded travel agent selling airline tickets at a discount.

8   To pay the bill.

9   Not reliable, might disappear to avoid paying debts.

10   A person who leaves a hotel quickly, without paying.

© Peter Collin Publishing
Based on the *Dictionary of Hotels, Tourism and Catering Management*
ISBN 0-948549-40-8

Travel quiz

HOW MANY OF these questions can you answer?

Questions

1. What is the currency of Morocco?

2. It's 12 o'clock noon in London. What time is it in New York?

3. Which city would you visit to see Michelangelo's David?

4. Which one of the pyramids is the largest?

5. Where is the unfinished cathedral of the Sagrada Familia?

6. How tall is the Eiffel Tower to within 10 metres?

7. Who are the four American presidents whose faces can be seen on Mount Rushmore?

8. What is the name of the fastest commercial aircraft in the world?

9. What volcano can you see from the city of Naples?

10. Which language has the most native speakers?

11. Where would you see women wearing saris?

12. What is the capital of Venezuela?

13. Where would you find the Hudson river?

14. Which country receives the largest number of tourists each year?

15. Which river contains the Lorely?

Extension. Work with a partner and write a travel and tourism quiz. Make sure you know the answers. Then ask another pair of students the questions.

© Peter Collin Publishing
Based on the *Dictionary of Hotels, Tourism and Catering Management*
ISBN 0-948549-40-8

Communicative Crossword 1 sheet A

This crossword is not complete: you have only half the words. The other half are on sheet B. Check that you know the words in your crossword. Then work with a partner who has sheet B to complete the two crosswords. Follow these three rules:

1 Speak only in English.

2 Don't say the word in the crossword.

3 Don't show your partner the crossword.

> *'What's 1 across?'*
> → across, ↓ down

Communicative Crossword 1   sheet B

This crossword is not complete: you have only half the words. The other half are on sheet A. Check that you know the words in your crossword. Then work with a partner who has sheet A to complete the two crosswords. Follow these three rules:

1	Speak only in English.
2	Don't say the word in the crossword.
3	Don't show your partner the crossword.

> 'What's 1 across?'
> → across, ↓ down

¹C	H	²E	E	³S	E	■	4		⁵S		6
L	■		■		■	■		■	L	■	
⁷E			8		■	⁹E	X	C	E	S	S
A	■	10				■			E	■	
¹¹N	¹²O	R	T	H	■	¹³A	¹⁴S	A	P	■	
■	F	■		■			P	¹⁵S	■		
16	F			17			O		■	■	
■	E		■		■		R	18		■	■
¹⁹P	R	²⁰E	P	A	Y	■	²¹T	H	E	M	E
	■	F	■	■	■	■		■		■	■
22		F					²³R				24
	■	I	■	■	■	■	U	■	■	■	
²⁵O	C	C	A	S	I	O	N	A	L	■	
	■	I	■		■	■	N	■	■	■	
	■	²⁶E	X	H	I	B	I	T	²⁷I	O	N
	■	N	■	■	■		N	■	L	■	
28		T				■	²⁹G	O	L	F	■

© Peter Collin Publishing
Based on the *Dictionary of Hotels, Tourism and Catering Management*
ISBN 0-948549-40-8

Communicative Crossword 2   sheet A

This crossword is not complete: you have only half the words. The other half are on sheet B. Check that you know the words in your crossword. Then work with a partner who has sheet B to complete the two crosswords. Follow these three rules:

| 1 | Speak only in English. |

| 2 | Don't say the word in the crossword. |

| 3 | Don't show your partner the crossword. |

'What's 1 across?'
→ across, ↓ down

Communicative Crossword 2   sheet B

This crossword is not complete: you have only half the words. The other half are on sheet A. Check that you know the words in your crossword. Then work with a partner who has sheet A to complete the two crosswords. Follow these three rules:

1 | Speak only in English

2 | Don't say the word in the crossword.

3 | Don't show your partner the crossword.

'What's one across?'
→ across, ↓ down

¹E	X	²C	U	³R	S	I	O	N			⁴D
C		A		O						⁵I	C	E
⁶O	U	T	G	O	I	N	⁷G		N		M
N		E		M			⁸		T		A
O		R			⁹				E		N
M		¹⁰I							R		D
¹¹Y	E	N					¹²L	I	N	E	
		G						A		¹³
¹⁴P			¹⁵			¹⁶M	I	L	E	S
O										
¹⁷L										
I							¹⁸			
¹⁹C							²⁰		²¹	
Y										
							²²			
²³L	A	N	D	S	²⁴C	A	P	E		
A										
²⁵W						²⁶			

© Peter Collin Publishing
Based on the *Dictionary of Hotels, Tourism and Catering Management*
ISBN 0-948549-40-8

Communicative Crossword 3 sheet A

This crossword is not complete: you have only half the words. The other half are on sheet B. Check that you know the words in your crossword. Then work with a partner who has sheet B to complete the two crosswords. Follow these three rules:

1 | Speak only in English.

2 | Don't say the word in the crossword.

3 | Don't show your partner the crossword.

> *'What's 1 across?'*
> → across, ↓ down

The crossword grid (letters filled in):

- 2 down: R E F R I G E R A T E
- 8 across: S T R I K E
- 13 across: W R I T E
- 12 down: D E S S
- 15 across: S E A T
- 16 down: A T
- 18 across: C O D E
- 21 across: E X T R A
- 21 down: E R T T
- 28 across: T E R T I A R Y (with 27/26 A ... T E R T I A R Y)
- 19 down: A L I N K
- 20 down: L I N K
- 25 down: E N T R Y
- 30 across: F L Y
- 31 across: Y E A R
- 32 across: R A N G

© Peter Collin Publishing
Based on the *Dictionary of Hotels, Tourism and Catering Management*
ISBN 0-948549-40-8

Communicative Crossword 3   sheet B

This crossword is not complete: you have only half the words. The other half are on sheet A. Check that you know the words in your crossword. Then work with a partner who has sheet A to complete the two crosswords. Follow these three rules:

1 Speak only in English.

2 Don't say the word in the crossword.

3 Don't show your partner the crossword.

> *'What's 1 across?'*
> → across, ↓ down

¹E	X	P	²R	E	S	S			³P	A	S	⁴S
X									L			U
⁵C	O	F	F	E	⁶E				U			S
I					X		⁷A	G	E	N	T	
⁸S					E		S					A
E					⁹C	R	A	¹⁰S	H			I
					U		¹¹P	A				N
12		13			T		L					A
					I		¹⁴F	A	X			B
15		16			¹⁷V	O	I	D				L
		18			E		N		19	20		E
21							G					
						²²R	E	²³D				
			²⁴K	A	R	A	O	K		²⁵E	
				26		T		I				
27		28				I		R	29			
30						N		³¹Y				
			32			G						

© Peter Collin Publishing
Based on the *Dictionary of Hotels, Tourism and Catering Management*
ISBN 0-948549-40-8

Peter Collin Publishing
Vocabulary Record Sheet

WORD	CLASS	NOTES Translation or definition, example...

© Peter Collin Publishing
Based on the *Dictionary of Hotels, Tourism and Catering Management*
ISBN 0-948549-40-8

Answers

Recipe ~ crab soup p.3
1. warm 2. mash 3. liquidize 4. simmer 5. chop 6. strain
7. peel 8. combine 9. stir 10. boil

Opposites ~ travel & tourism p.4
Exercise 1 add/subtract advance/postpone arrival/departure
cancel/confirm cheap/expensive decrease/increase
disembark/embark double/single early/late guest/host
incoming/outgoing land/take off loss/profit
overcharge/undercharge receive/send

Exercise 2 1. landed 2. postpone 3. overcharged
4. disembark 5. late 6. profit 7. confirm 8. added
9. incoming 10. expensive 11. guests 12. double
13. arrival/departure 14. decreases 15. send

Recipes ~ gratin potatoes & apple crumble p.5
Gratin potatoes
1 Warm the milk to just less than boiling point and leave it to one side.
2 While it is cooking, peel the potatoes and then slice thinly.
3 Put the potatoes in the dish and season them with the salt, pepper and nutmeg.
4 Blend the egg and half the cheese into the milk.
5 Stir the mixture into the potatoes.
6 Rub a dish with garlic and butter.
7 Put the rest of the cheese on top.
8 Bake it in a medium oven for 45 minutes.

Apple crumble
1 Peel, core and slice the apples.
2 Put them in a pan with the water and the nutmeg and cook them until they form a puree.
3 Meanwhile, rub the butter into the flour until it looks like breadcrumbs.
4 Stir the sugar into the flour and butter mix; this is the crumble.
5 Remove the puree from the heat and leave it to cool for five minutes.
6 When it has cooled, add a little sugar if necessary.
7 Put the puree into a buttered dish and cover it with the crumble.
8 Cook it under a medium grill until the butter melts and the top browns.

Pronunciation ~ word stress p.6
6 × ■□□	separate; catering; restaurant; shareholder; company; manager
12 × □■□	excursion; tomorrow; reception; divided; apartments; financial; insurance; effective; including; successful; allergic; tomato
5 × □□■	employees; recommend; vinaigrette; disagrees; guarantee
2 × ■□□□	supermarket; occupancy
5 × □■□□	available; facilities; gymnasium; convenient; asparagus
5 × □□■□	reservation; cancellation; situation; operations; avocado

Business ~ prepositions 1 p.7
1 Our accredited agent in Bali is Mr Rodas: contact him and he can act ~~in~~ **on** our behalf.
2 At the moment we are computerizing ~~of~~ our administrative systems.
3 The Plains H<xel is affiliated **to** our group.
4 We need to meet again on Thursday: is 9.30 a convenient time ~~to~~ **for** you?
5 The waitresses served ~~to~~ the 250 diners very efficiently.
6 We try to offer a flexible service, adapting **to** the needs of our individual customers.
7 Thank you for your order, which will receive ~~of~~ our immediate attention.
8 The ~~in~~ **on**-site courier is very reliable: we have been working with her for six years.
9 We only use reputable carriers, which means we can guarantee you an exceptional level ~~in~~ **of** quality.
10 This item is not available in the shops: it can be bought only ~~in~~ **by** mail order.
11 I'm afraid we do not have any double rooms available ~~on~~ **in** the first week of August.
12 She runs a flourishing tour company organizing adventure holidays ~~at~~ **for** senior citizens.
13 The new system operative becomes operational ~~in~~ **on** June 1st
14 I have faxed you my provisional acceptance **of** the terms you offer.
15 He's the kind of person you can trust ~~for~~ **to** do the job, absolutely reliable.
16 We had to ask our lawyer **for** professional advice about the contract
17 Eventually we would like to install ~~in~~ an indoor swimming pool, but that's a long-term project.
18 He has the sole agency ~~to~~ **for** Ascot car hire in this region.
19 After the fire they looked **at** the policies and discovered that the hotel was uninsured.
20 Each hotel manager is accountable **to** the regional manager.

50 foods ~ categories p.8
apple-fruit apricot-fruit asparagus-vegetable avocado-fruit
bacon-meat banana-fruit basil-seasoning beef-meat carrot-vegetable cheese-dairy product chicken-poultry cod-fish
courgette-vegetable cream-dairy product cucumber-vegetable
duck-poultry garlic-seasoning goose-poultry grape-fruit
grapefruit-fruit haddock-fish hake-fish lamb-meat lettuce-vegetable milk-dairy product onion-vegetable oregano-seasoning parsley-seasoning peach-fruit pear-fruit pepper-vegetable/seasoning pineapple-fruit plaice-fish pork-meat
potato-vegetable raspberry-fruit red mullet-fish rosemary-seasoning salmon-fish sole-fish spinach-vegetable
strawberry-fruit thyme-seasoning tomato-fruit/vegetable
trout-fish tuna-fish turbot-fish turkey-poultry veal-meat
yoghurt-dairy product

Cooking verbs p.9
1. bake; *k* 2. blanch; *p* 3. braise; *o* 4. caramelize; *n*
5. carve; *m* 6. chill; *q* 7. cream; *r* 8. deep-fry; *v* 9. dice; *u*
10. flambé; *t* 11. flavour; *s* 12. fricasee; *l* 13. fry; *d*
14. garnish; *c* 15. grate; *b* 16. grill; *a* 17. grind; *e*

18. liquidize; *f* 19. marinade; *z* 20. parboil; *j*
21. poach; *i* 22. roast; *h* 23. sauté; *g* 24. slice; *w*
25. steam; *x* 26. stuff; *y*

Odd one out p.10

1 <u>cuisine</u>: the others are all jobs
2 <u>land</u>: the others all happen at the beginning of a flight
3 <u>holiday</u>: the others all refer specifically to travel
4 <u>message</u>: the others are all ways of communicating
5 <u>cheque</u>: the others are all documents which record transactions
6 <u>currency</u>: the others are all ways of paying
7 <u>lamb</u>: the others are all poultry
8 <u>claret</u>: the others are spirits
9 <u>cheap</u>: the others all mean that no payment is made
10 <u>immigrant</u>: the other's stays are only temporary
11 <u>law</u>: the others all refer to ticket classes
12 <u>swimming pool</u>: the others are often found in hotel rooms
13 <u>magazine</u>: the others are connected with reservations
14 <u>purchase</u>: the others are temporary
15 <u>individual</u>: the others are types of hotel room
16 <u>guest</u>: the others are jobs
17 <u>slice</u>: the others are ways of cooking
18 <u>creditors</u>: the others are assets
19 <u>manager</u>: the others are buyers
20 <u>yam</u>: the others are currencies

Business ~ prepositions 2 p.11

1 We are analysing ~~of~~ the market potential for golfing holidays.
2 When we advertised for a new restaurant manager sixty people applied **for** the job.
3 The chairman has asked all managers to attend ~~in~~ the meeting.
4 Communicating **with** head office has been quicker since we installed the fax.
5 He tried to contact his office ~~with~~ **by** phone.
6 The business is controlled ~~for~~ **by** a company based in Luxembourg.
7 We estimate current sales ~~in~~ **at** only 60% of last year's.
8 The government foresees a big increase in tourism ~~in~~ next year.
9 This product is guaranteed ~~during~~ **for** twelve months.
10 The accounts department handles ~~with~~ all the cash.
11 We are inquiring **into** the background of the new hotel proprietor.
12 We interviewed ~~of~~ ten candidates, but did not find anyone suitable.
13 The company is spending thousands of pounds ~~for~~ **to** launch a new travel service.
14 There is a system of bonus payments which are linked ~~at~~ **to** your productivity figures.
15 The restaurant has maintained the same volume of business in spite **of** the recession.
16 Not all the hotels in the chain are participating ~~of~~ **in** this special Christmas offer.
17 We are promoting these new holidays on the TV, on the radio, ~~on~~ **in** the press and on posters in the underground.
18 I certainly would not recommend ~~to~~ Miss Smith for the job.
19 Candidates should report **to** our London office for interview.
20 The company transports millions of tons of goods ~~on~~ **by** rail each year.

Staff p.12

1 <u>casual</u>: for a short period not regular
2 <u>in-house</u>: working inside a company's building
3 <u>live-in</u>: living in the building where (one) works
4 <u>self-employed</u>: working for oneself
5 <u>go on strike</u>: to stop working because there is a disagreement with management
6 <u>short-handed</u>: with not enough staff
7 <u>assign</u>: to give someone a job of work
8 <u>dismiss</u>: to remove an employee from a job
9 <u>hire and fire</u>: to engage new staff and dismiss existing staff frequently
10 <u>promote</u>: to give someone a more important job
11 <u>qualify</u>: to follow a specialized course and pass examinations so that you can do a certain job
12 <u>supervise</u>: to watch work carefully to see if it is well done
13 <u>stop</u>: to take money out of someone's wages before they receive them
14 <u>staff</u>: to provide workers for an organization

Travel crossword p.13

¹F	L	²I	G	H	³T			⁴T	⁵R	I	⁶P	
R		N			A			O			⁷L	E	G
⁸E	A	S	T		X			R			A	
I		U			⁹I	N	B	O	U	N	D	
¹⁰G	A	R	A	G	E							¹¹C
H		A				¹²S	¹³A	F	A	¹⁴R	I	O
¹⁵T	E	N	T			R			E			M
		C			¹⁶C	R	U	I	S	E		P
¹⁷F	L	E	E	T		I			E			A
L						V		¹⁸T	R	A	I	N
¹⁹O	F	²⁰F		²¹S	T	A	R	V				I
O		A		E		L		E				O
²²R	E	N	T	A	L		²³R	I	D	D	E	N

Hotel reservations p.14

Conversation 1

o Barnes Hotel. Good morning. Can I help you?
• Yes. I'd like to make a reservation.
o What dates would you like to reserve for?
• The 16th and 17th of June. A single room.
o With a bathroom?
• Yes, please.
o So that's a single room with bathroom for two nights, the 16th and 17th of June.
• That's correct.
o Good. Could you give me your name?
• Andrew Orpheo.
o Could you spell your surname?
• Certainly. O-R-P-H-E-O.
o Orpheo. And how will you be paying?
• By Visa.
o Can you give me the number?
• Yes, it's 3956 7254 9984 9876.
o 3956 7254 9984 9876. And what's the expiry date?
• 04/99.
o Thank you very much. We'll look forward to seeing you on the 16th.
• Thank you.

Conversation 2
o Barnes Hotel. Good afternoon. Can I help you?
• Yes, do you have any rooms free for tonight?
o Single or double?
• Double, please.
o Yes, we do have a couple of rooms.
• What are your rates?
o £42.50 a night including breakfast.
• OK. That's fine. We'll be there in half an hour.
o Could I have your name for the reservation?
• Davies.
o Thank you Mr Davies. We'll look forward to seeing you in about half an hour.
• Thank you. Goodbye.

Opposites ~ tastes p.15
Exercise 1. sweet/dry: fresh/frozen: fresh/stale: still/sparkling: tasteless/tasty: rare/well-done: overdone/underdone: bland/spicy: sweet/salty: sweet/sour: tough/tender: raw/cooked
Exercise 2. 1. dry 2. stale 3. sour 4. rare 5. frozen 6. sparkling 7. undercooked 8. raw 9. salty 10. tasty 11. tough 12. spicy

Air travel p.16
Exercise 1
1 I arrived at the airport.
2 I checked in.
3 I went through passport control.
4 I bought a bottle of wine in the duty free shop.
5 I joined the other passengers at the gate.
6 We boarded the plane.
7 It took off.
8 I had lunch and watched an in-flight movie.
9 Three hours later we landed.
10 We disembarked.
11 I went to baggage claim and picked up my case.
12 I left the airport.

Exercise 2. 1. advanced 2. booked 3. delayed 4. departed 5. missed 6. upgraded 7. grounded 8. routed 9. stopped over 10. taxied 11. touched down 12. scheduled

Pronunciation ~ present simple p.17
Group A /s/: accommodates; assists; escorts; restricts; starts; overlooks; permits; takes; boasts
Group B /z/: flies; reboards; drives; allows; caters; gives; lives; owns; fills
Group C /ɪz/: arranges; attaches; passes; charges; manages; reaches; supervises

Tax & accounts ~ adjectives p.18
1. duty-free 2. unpaid 3. taxable 4. profitable 5. inclusive 6. self-financed 7. labour-intensive 8. exempt 9. convertible 10. round 11. allowable 12. deductible 13. tax-free 14. gross 15. current

Cash or cheque? p.19
1. Cash
i hard cash = money in notes and coins, as opposed to cheques or credit cards
ii petty cash = small amounts of money
iii ready cash = money which is immediately available for payment
iv cash desk = place in a store where you pay for the goods bought

v cash dispenser = machine which gives out money when a special card is inserted and instructions given
vi cash register = machine which shows and adds the prices of items bought, with a drawer for keeping the cash received
vii cash terms = terms which apply if the customer pays cash
viii cash flow = cash which comes into a company from sales or goes out in purchases or overhead expenditure
ix cash settlement = paying a bill in cash
x cash card = card used to obtain money from a cash dispenser

2. Cheque
i crossed cheque = cheque with two lines across it showing that it can only be deposited at a bank and not exchanged for cash
ii uncrossed cheque = cheque which can be cashed anywhere
iii blank cheque = cheque with the amount of money and the payee left blank, but signed by the drawer
iv bouncing cheque = cheque which cannot be cashed because the person writing it has not enough money in the account to pay it
v sign a cheque = sign on the front of a cheque to show that you authorize the bank to pay the money from your account
vi cheque card = plastic card from a bank which guarantees payment of a cheque
vii cash a cheque = exchange a cheque for cash
viii endorse a cheque = sign a cheque on the back to show that you accept it
ix deposit a cheque = pay a cheque into your account
x stop a cheque = ask a bank not to pay a cheque you have written

Kitchen crossword p.20

¹F	I	²L	L	E	³T		⁴B	R	E	⁵A	D
E		A			O		R			P	
⁶E	G	G		⁷S	A	L	A	D		P	
D		E		S			N			L	
	⁸F	R	⁹U	I	T		¹⁰D	R	¹¹I	E	¹²D
	A		N					Y	N		I
¹³S	T	U	F	F		¹⁴C			¹⁵G	I	N
I			I			O			R		N
¹⁶T	A	¹⁷R	T			¹⁸F	R	E	E	Z	E
T		Y		¹⁹J		F			D		R
²⁰I	C	E		²¹U	T	E	N	S	I	L	
N				I		E			E		²²F
G				C					N		E
²³S	A	U	C	E		²⁴H	E	A	T	E	D

Anagrams 1 p.21
1 ADDRESS
2 DOUBLE
3 MAIL
4 INTERNATIONAL
5 NIGHT
6 INVOICE

7 SEASON
8 TAPAS
9 RECEPTION
10 AVAILABLE
11 TERMINUS
12 INTERPRET
13 OMELETTE
14 NOISE

Finance ~ verbs p.22

a. break even b. crash c. cover d. audit e. account for
f. subsidize g. save h. budget i. yield j. invest k. forecast
l. lease

Prices & payment ~ adjectives p.23

1. supplementary 2. popular 3. chargeable 4. advance
5. non-refundable. 6. refundable 7. exclusive 8. optional
9. all-in 10. moderate 11. cut-price 12. inexpensive
13. off-season 14. prohibitive 15. off-peak

Business ~ two-word expressions p.24

1. joint venture 2. cash flow 3. legal tender 4. exchange rate
5. working capital 6. balance sheet 7. hard currency
8. profit margin 9. disposable income 10. black market
11. marketing mix 12. credit card 13. bank statement
14. business lunch 15. red tape

Anagrams 2 p.25

1 DIARY
2 IMPORT
3 SMUGGLE
4 EXTRA
5 MILLION
6 BREAKFAST
7 AVOCADO
8 RESTAURANT
9 KITCHEN
10 ACCOMMODATION
11 TEMPERATURE
12 INTEREST
13 OPTION
14 NORDIC

Word association p.26

1. baggage 2. flight 3. tax 4. telephone 5. wine 6. ticket

Active to passive p.27

1 10% of our revenue is allocated to publicity.
2 Women are forbidden to go into the temple.
3 My hotel room was broken into and my wallet was stolen.
4 The visitors were shown around the cathedral by a guide.
5 Expenditure has been broken down into hotel, travel and entertainment costs.
6 The wedding reception will be held in the Blue Room.
7 $2,500 is being allocated to furnishing the guests' lounge.
8 When the first booking was made the hotel was still being built.
9 The dining rooms are being renovated for the new season.
10 A new travel service will be launched next month.
11 I was transferred to another flight because the one I was on had been overbooked.
12 The coach needs to be serviced every six months.
13 The flight would have been cancelled if this information had been received earlier.
14 The hotel will have been furnished by the end of August.

Abbreviations p.28

1. gin and tonic 2. errors and omissions excepted
3. Estimated Time of Arrival 4. Public Relations
5. Electronic Funds Transfer 6. Food and Beverage
7. European Currency Unit 8. as soon as possible 9. Annual
General Meeting 10. Value Added Tax 11. Strengths,
Weaknesses, Opportunities and Threats 12. Short Take-Off
and Landing 13. Point Of Sale 14. Inclusive Tour (also
Information Technology) 15. Letter of Credit 16. Annual
Percentage Rate 17. bed and breakfast 18. Computer
Reservation System 19. or near offer 20. barbecue

Marketing ~ adjectives p.29

1. popular 2. toll-free 3. seasonal 4. down-market 5. slack
6. backup 7. socio-economic 8. promotional 9. domestic 10.
average 11. regular 12. complimentary
13. discretionary 14. elastic 15. upmarket

Prices & payments ~ verbs p.30

a. shop around b. include c. price d. bargain e. quote
f. pay down g. refund h. discount i. slash j. deduct
k. invoice l. accept

Food & drink ~ French in English p.31

1. brut 2. digestif 3. plat du jour 4. plongeur 5. vinaigrette
6. à la carte 7. à la mode 8. château 9. chef de cuisine 10.
de luxe 11. soupçon 12. chambré 13. en pension
14. sauté 15. cordon bleu 16. table d'hôte 17. maître d'hôtel
18. bouquet garni 19. nouvelle cuisine
20. hors-d'oeuvre 21. traiteur

Pronunciation ~ past simple p.32

Group A /t/: addressed; backed out; faxed; announced; asked;
double-booked; equipped; processed; fixed; launched
Group B /d/: warned; cancelled; telephoned; received;
changed; smuggled; trained; postponed; called
Group C /ɪd/: diverted; visited; updated; included; translated;
allocated; recruited; lifted; recommended; invited

Hotels ~ adjectives p.33

1. luxurious 2. alternative 3. self-service 4. dedicated
5. adjoining 6. noisy 7. short-stay 8. sunny 9. surrounding
10. vacant 11. en suite 12. non-residents 13. self catering
14. comfortable 15. private

Slang p.34

1. steep 2. backhander 3. cheers 4. moonlight 5. starving
6. loo 7. bucket shop 8. pick up the tab 9. fly-by-night
10. skipper

Travel quiz p.35

1. the dirham 2. seven o'clock in the morning 3. Florence 4.
the Great Pyramid of Khufu at Giza 5. Barcelona 6. 300
metres 7. George Washington, Thomas Jefferson, Abraham
Lincoln, Theodore Roosevelt 8. Concord 9. Vesuvius
10. Chinese 11. India 12. Caracas 13. New York
14. France 15. the Rhine